Very special thanks to Roy and Liz Steinke, Benaya and LeRoy Allison, Karen Lile, Judith Branch, Megan Allison and everyone else who backed the creation of this book. Without your support this dream would never have come true. Fair winds to you all!

The Greatest Captain in the World!

Written, adapted and created by Johann Steinke.

Sailor stories by Joel Ruud.

Illustrated by Andy Catling.

Fair Winds!

Johann Steinke

In a town by the shore near a seaside store
A family from the country walked by.
The parents wished to shop
As the children did stop
To stare at the masts in the sky.

Dad said, "Go along, we won't be long
And let us know when you're through.
But don't trust the seaman
And the yarns they are weavin'
For none of their stories are true."

So they raced to a ship, just back from a trip, all tied to the great big dock,

When they spied an old sailor, trying to be a tailor, as he sewed up the end of his sock.

He eyed them with a sneer as the children stood in fear,
And asked "What're you on about?"
They said, "We don't know", and so turned to go,
When the sailor stood up with a ...

"Now don't you go, or you'll never know,
   Why our captain is the greatest in the world!
So change your tack and come on back,
   And I'll set your mind a whirl."

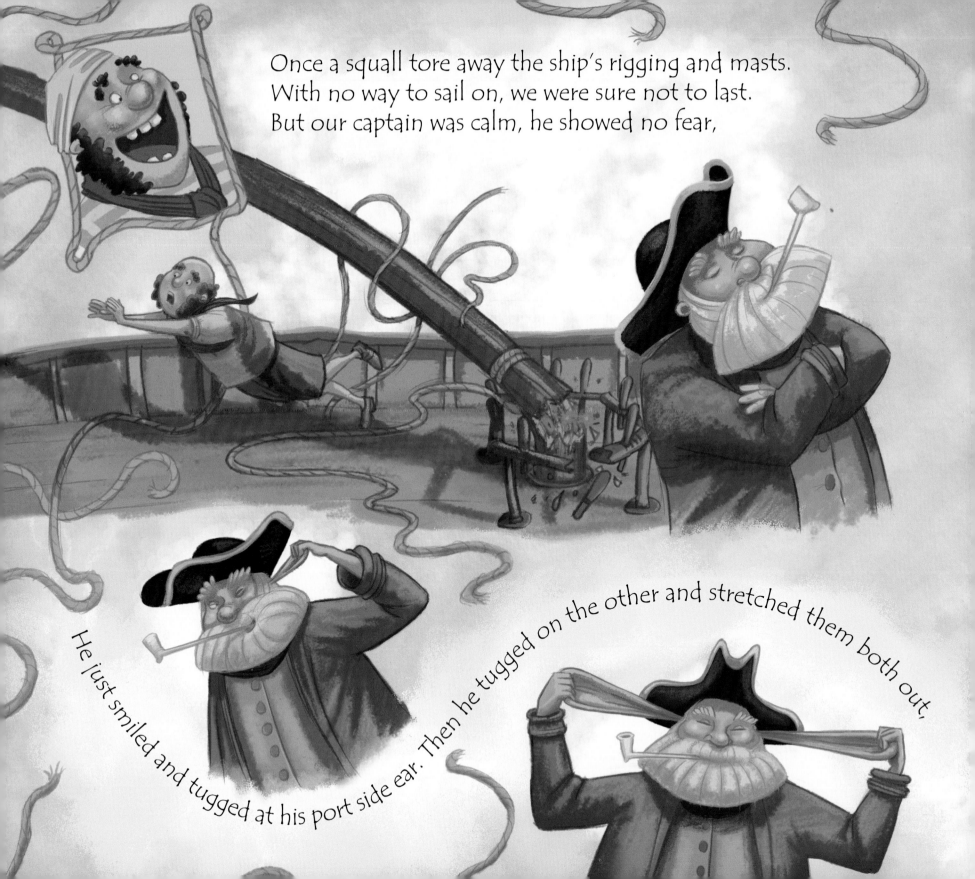

Once a squall tore away the ship's rigging and masts.
With no way to sail on, we were sure not to last.
But our captain was calm, he showed no fear,

He just smiled and tugged at his port side ear. Then he tugged on the other and stretched them both out,

Till the crew joined in with a heave and a shout.

They were stretched three times around the whole ship,
When our captain let fly with a twirl and a flip.

And wouldn't you know it, those ears caught a gust, and the bow shot ahead with a surge and a thrust.

Another sailor stated, "So it's yarns you want to hear?
Well I've got a story that makes every sailor cheer."

One time our captain set foot on dry land,
A stranger experience he never did have.
For the ground he was on wouldn't move or budge,
Not with a kick nor a hearty nudge.

Then along came a critter that slithered cross his path, boldly risking our great captain's wrath.

What a thing to see this slug on the ground,
They stared at each other not making a sound.

Then with a fizzle, the slug melted in a haze,

This was the power of our captain's salty gaze.

Down came a shipmate, trying to top the other two,
"Well how about the time our captain saved the crew?"

We were out on the ocean, whaling at the time,
When this wave comes to sink us and take us in our prime.
Now most would have cowered, maybe tried to steer away,
But not our captain, no sir, no way.

He ran from the tiller to the boat's bluff bow,

took in a breath of air with a deep throated growl.

He puffed out his cheeks like a whale gulping krill,
And blasted out air with a force and a will.
Then he blew a big hole in the middle of that wave,
He sailed on through it, and so we were saved.

A small, slender sailor jumped in from the rail,
"Now here is a tale that'll make you go pale!"

Why you've never heard tell of a wave so high!
It snuffed out the sun, blotting out the whole sky.

The captain called out, "Batten down the hatches,
Below decks crew, and secure those latches!"

With that he raced to the ship's starboard side,
Yanked the anchor off the rail, and took a big dive.

He pulled down the ship, swimming under the wave!
When we got back to the surface we knew we were saved.

In the log he later wrote, "Wave headed our direction,
But now steering true after a slight course correction."

Another tar appeared, who was tall and big around,
"I've got a story that will knock you to the ground."
We once saw a flag, with skull and crossbones white,
Flying from a ship that was looking for a fight.
The pirates were coming, for gold to plunder,
Shooting at our boat to split her asunder.

They wanted us all to reach for the sky,
But our captain didn't care, he was staring at a fly.
He snapped up that pest, with his fathom-long tongue,
Then he spat it at the pirates just for fun.

The fly shot into their ship so rotten,
Blasted clean through and sank her to the bottom.

Another sailor showed, shouldering a gun,
"The story's not through, it's only just begun."

On a blood red dawn we saw a pirate fleet,
Hundreds of ships in rows so neat.

Now it was certain we were all going to die,

When our captain uncrinkled his one crinkly eye.

The pirates just stared in true disbelief,
The colors in that eye, gave them such grief.
A prettier sight they never would see,

No treasure in the world could give them more glee.
They say they stayed forever in their den,
Never yearning for jewels nor gold again.

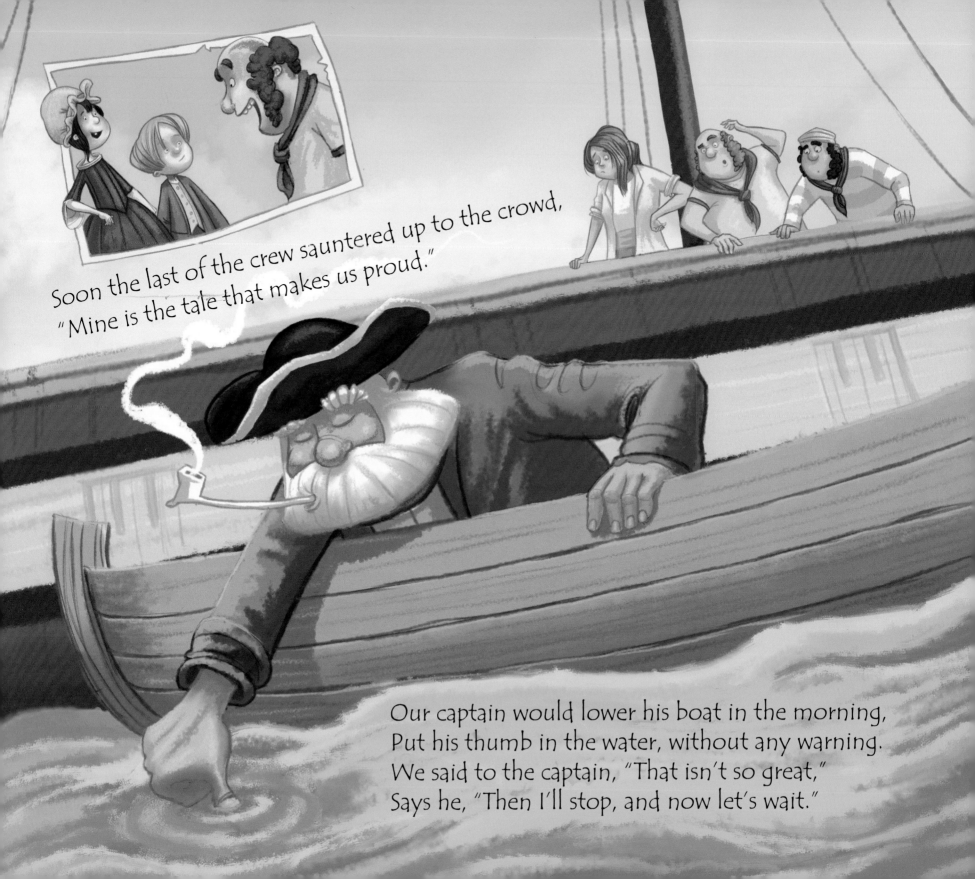

Soon the last of the crew sauntered up to the crowd,
"Mine is the tale that makes us proud."

Our captain would lower his boat in the morning,
Put his thumb in the water, without any warning.
We said to the captain, "That isn't so great,"
Says he, "Then I'll stop, and now let's wait."

And so we stared two hours or more,
Trying to figure out what the wait was for,

When up came all the monsters of the deep,
A-glaring and a-groaning, and not a one asleep.

The captain yelled, to each and every one,
"It's time you grow up, no more sucking on my thumb."

And with the sailors gathered round came a horrific sound
As the mate began to bark and spit
"Avast yer yarns and this I warns,
our captain's bringing the cargo on a ship."

The sailors toed the line in record time
As the children went back to their folks
They told what they'd heard, every single word,
But the parents said those stories were just jokes.

"Their imaginations roam, now let us go home," as the wagon went clackity clack,
And as the road began to wind, the children looked behind.

To see that great captain with the supply ship on his back!

What are those sailors doing?

Caulking- This is what the sailor in the background is doing when he is hammering into the boat. He is actually hammering in oakum (tarred fibers) to fill in the gaps in the planks. This is what makes a wooden ship mostly watertight... mostly.

Diversity- Historically many ships had people from many different cultures and places on board. On a boat sailors were more interested in what type of person you were and how well you could do your job and help the ship and crew. Where you were from or what you believed didn't matter so much for them. This means that ships would often take on people from all over and it made for very interesting encounters when a ship would come in from overseas.

Whaling- Yep, people hunted whales historically. In native cultures it was for food and survival. In the west it was for the oil in the whales' blubber (fat). This oil was really good for lighting lamps. Whales were nearly hunted to extinction (meaning hunted until there were no more) but thankfully today they are protected. We need to keep protecting whales and all wild animals on our planet, or they will not survive.

Sewing- What, sailors sewed? Well yes. You would never throw out anything on a boat and if a piece of clothing had a simple hole or tear in it. It made more sense to sew it up. Sailors were great at sewing because they would often make and repair their own sails onboard.

Guns- Guns are a sailor's word for cannons. But wait, these sailors look like merchant sailors who are shipping things for trading and for selling. Why would they need guns? Well, their cargo might be very valuable and people like pirates or enemy nations and groups might want them, so guns can help fight them off. Plus, a ship that could show that it could defend itself was less likely to be attacked or taken advantage of. Lastly, guns were also used for saluting other ships and forts and on special occasions.

Barrels- Also known as casks. Many many things were shipped in barrels in the past. Food and liquids were stored in barrels. They could be rolled, stacked, and broken down when they were empty. They were very handy to store things in when all you had was human power to move them.

Women- Today, anyone can become a sailor, but historically women were not allowed to be part of the crew the way we have shown in our book. However, there are many historical accounts of women coming aboard ships and assisting the ship and crew, fighting in battles, and even disguising themselves as men to become a normal member of the crew. The women crew members in our book are our symbolic attempt to acknowledge these brave women, and also the many incredible women sailors and captains out there in the world today.

Glossary

Yarns- Sailors' stories, usually exaggerated.

Tack- The way the sails are positioned to catch the wind (Usually on one side or the other). So in order to catch the wind on the other side of the ship, you would have to change direction, so when the sailor says, "Change your tack," he is poetically telling the children to, "Turn around"

Squall- A small area of intense wind and sometimes rain. The sudden change in wind can destroy rigging and masts if a sailor has too much sail set.

Rigging and Masts- Masts are the big poles that hold up the yards. Yards are the big poles on the masts that run horizontal and perpendicular to the ship. Rigging is all the sails and ropes attached to the yards and masts.

Port and Starboard- If you are facing forward on a boat then the port side is to your left and the starboard side is to your right.

Bow- The front of the boat.

Salty- When you are out at sea and constantly getting splashed by the salty sea water, as the seawater dries, it will leave sea salt all over your skin and clothes. This was why the old sailors were sometimes described as "salty" or even "crusty"

Tiller- A stick attach to a rudder that allows you to steer. In our book the captain is actual using a sort of oar as his means of steering, just like in old whaling paintings.

Bluff Bow- This means a broad, flat front for the boat, but the sailor is just being poetic. In reality, the whaling boat they are in does not have a bluff bow.

Krill- Shrimp-like animals that whales eat.

Batten down the hatches- Hatches (openings in the ship's deck) were often left open, or had a grating over them that allowed air in. This is great when it's hot, or when you need to air out the areas below, but horrible in bad weather for water can splash in and sink your boat. Sailors would put water-proof cloth over the openings and then "batten" them in place by pinning the skins to the hatch with wedges.

Tar- Black, sticky, syrupy, stuff that smells great! Sailors would wipe tar on many parts of the rigging to keep water and moisture away. Their hands would get dirty and stained from the tar and so sometimes sailors were referred to as "Tars"

Fathom- One fathom equals 6 feet. This is a measurement used to tell how deep the water is.

Gun- Cannon. Cannons on ships were called guns... sailors have a different name for everything.

Avast- It means freeze, and stop what you are doing, but don't let go of anything!

Toed the Line- When naval sailors lined up for inspection, they would have a specific line (of the many lines of caulking that surrounded every deck plank) on the deck that they would have to put their toes on. In our book, we are saying that the sailors are getting back to the jobs and work very quickly.

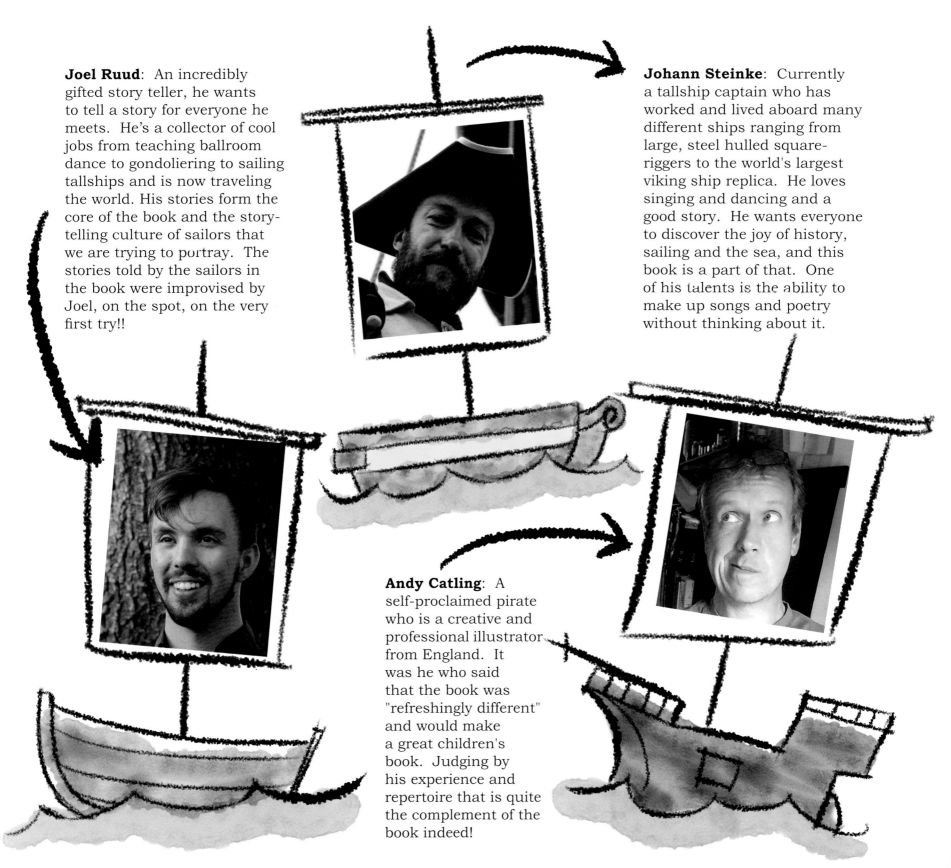

Joel Ruud: An incredibly gifted story teller, he wants to tell a story for everyone he meets. He's a collector of cool jobs from teaching ballroom dance to gondoliering to sailing tallships and is now traveling the world. His stories form the core of the book and the story-telling culture of sailors that we are trying to portray. The stories told by the sailors in the book were improvised by Joel, on the spot, on the very first try!!

Johann Steinke: Currently a tallship captain who has worked and lived aboard many different ships ranging from large, steel hulled square-riggers to the world's largest viking ship replica. He loves singing and dancing and a good story. He wants everyone to discover the joy of history, sailing and the sea, and this book is a part of that. One of his talents is the ability to make up songs and poetry without thinking about it.

Andy Catling: A self-proclaimed pirate who is a creative and professional illustrator from England. It was he who said that the book was "refreshingly different" and would make a great children's book. Judging by his experience and repertoire that is quite the complement of the book indeed!

You too can be a sailor!!

Go sail on a real-life tallship!! Feel the wind in your hair, hear the water rushing past, see the sails billowing in the wind. Experience the wonder and romance of the Age of Sail and learn why so many love these old boats!

To find some of our favorite tallships, hear about events, learn more about a sailor's life and the Greatest Captain in the World, please visit our website:

www.greatestcaptain.com

Or you can follow The Greatest Captain in the World on Facebook to keep up with what's new.

Also, check out your local maritime museum. If you are anywhere near the coast there are many wonderful museums that focus on the local maritime history. You might discover amazing events that occurred nearby, be able to see detailed models and paintings of amazing historical ships, or possibly even find real-life pirate treasure!

Finally, go look up your local yacht club and give them a call. Very often people have boats but are looking for people to join them on their day sails. Also, many yacht clubs are very inclusive and they really want to bring families into their sailing community